Float Like A Boat

The Aquatic Problem Solvers of Enchanted Brook

Michelle McKinney

Illustrated by Mousam Banerjee

Saguaro Press

ISBN - 979-8-9851963-4-4

In loving memory of my mother, who always believed I could do hard things.

It was a beautiful spring morning and the forest was abuzz with excitement. Mrs. Riverton had arrived from upstream to teach the newest littles of Enchanted Brook to swim.

"Hello everyone!" exclaimed Mrs. Riverton. "Thank you for the warm welcome. We're going to have so much fun in the water!" she said, smiling. "Lessons begin this afternoon. Before we get started, can anyone tell me what the first and most important step is in learning to swim?" Mrs. Riverton asked.

"Learning to blow bubbles!" shouted Cooper as he lowered his snout into a mud puddle and snorted. Everyone giggled as a big mud bubble popped, covering Cooper's face with sticky brown mud.

"Blowing bubbles is super fun! But when your mouth is under water, you should hold your breath, not blow it out," Mrs. Riverton replied. "Any other guesses?"

"I know! I know! Wearing our puddle jumpers!"
exclaimed Lily as she pulled on her favorite
polka dot puddle jumper.

"You are a puddle jumper, Lily!" Mrs. Riverton said. "You don't need that to swim! Puddle jumpers and arm floaties can actually be really dangerous. They put your body in the wrong position in the water, and prevent you from learning the first and MOST important step in learning to swim, which is..."

"Learning to float...
FLOAT LIKE A BOAT!"
said Mrs. Riverton.

"This is my friend, Marin, and together, we're going to teach you to do just that! We'll see you all this afternoon!"

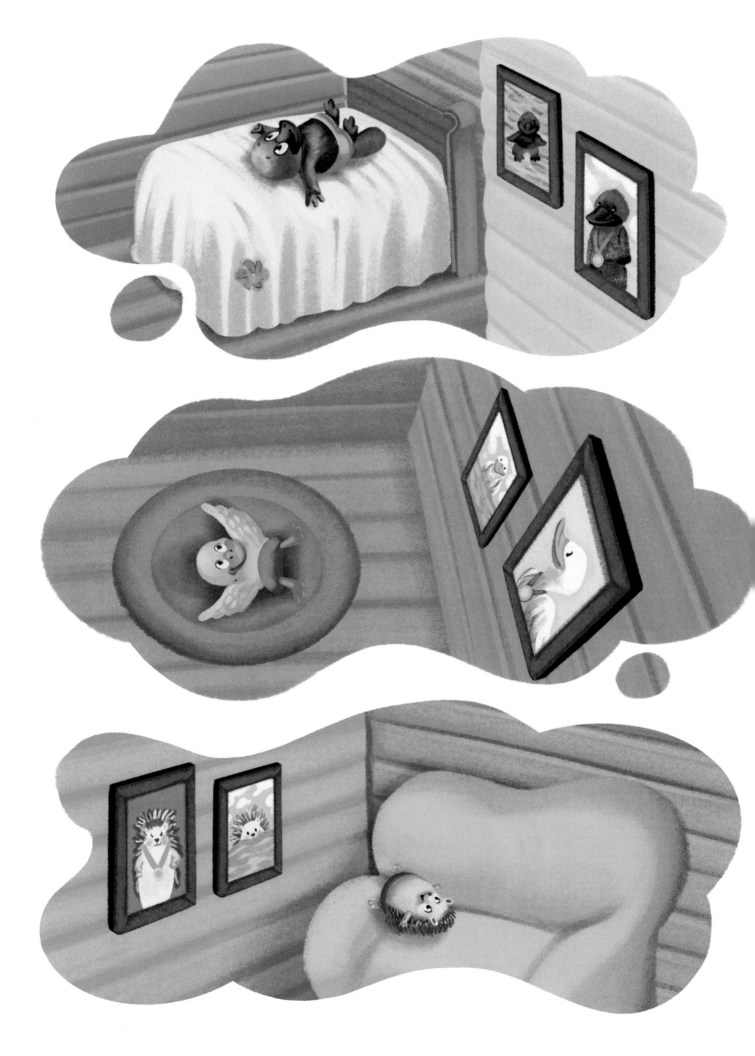

Best friends Webster, Mallory, and Quilliam couldn't wait for their first lesson. They descended from a long line of decorated aquatic problem solvers, and had been practicing their starfish position for weeks in anticipation of Mrs. Riverton's arrival.

While the three friends eagerly prepared for their first lesson, another friend, Beckett, wasn't feeling as excited for his first day.

"Momma? I think I changed my mind about swim lessons," Beckett said nervously. "My friends were all born to swim, but I just don't think it's my thing. Why can't I do gymnastics instead?!"

"Oh, buddy, I understand you're anxious about learning to swim." said Beckett's mom motioning for him to come sit with her.

"I signed you up for Mrs. Riverton's lessons to make sure you're safe around the water. Learning new things is hard, and you can do hard things!"

"C'mon, let's get going so you can watch some of your friend's lessons before it's your turn. I can't wait to watch you learn!" said Beckett's mom encouragingly as they left their burrow.

Beckett and his mom made their way down to the river, guided by the sound of loud cheering and clapping. All of Enchanted Brook had come out to encourage their littles on the first day of swim lessons.

It was Quilliam's turn and he was cool as a cucumber in his starfish position. Beckett wondered how he was able to float like that.

"It must be his small body."

"Wow, check out that starfish! You floated all on your own!" Mrs. Riverton exclaimed as she picked Quilliam up and gave him a high five. Quilliam smiled as his friends and family cheered him on.

"Alright, let's do it a few more times!" Mrs. Riverton said, laying Quilliam back in the water. Each time Quilliam practiced his float, he was able to hold it just a little bit longer than the time before. "Great job, Quilliam! That's it for today," said Mrs. Riverton.

One after another, Beckett's friends took their turn.

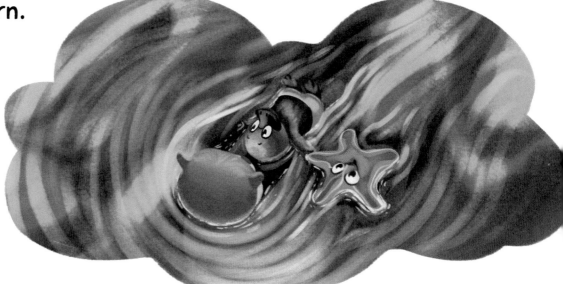

Each time, Beckett wondered how they were able to float like that.

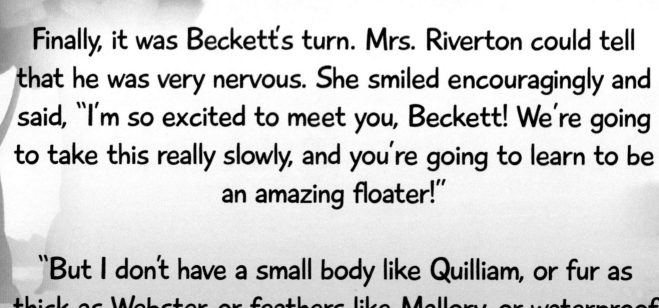

Finally, it was Beckett's turn. Mrs. Riverton could tell that he was very nervous. She smiled encouragingly and said, "I'm so excited to meet you, Beckett! We're going to take this really slowly, and you're going to learn to be an amazing floater!"

"But I don't have a small body like Quilliam, or fur as thick as Webster, or feathers like Mallory, or waterproof skin like Lily. How am I going to float?" Beckett asked with a tear rolling down his cheek.

"Can I tell you a secret?" Mrs. Riverton asked. "The key to floating isn't a small body, or thick fur, or feathers, or waterproof skin. The key to floating is staying calm and believing in yourself. You can do hard things! Let's take a deep breath together, and then you can show me."

Mrs. Riverton carried Beckett to the middle of the river and gave him a quick wink and a reassuring look. "You've got this!" she said, as she laid him back in the water. Marin clasped Beckett's hand as he opened his arms and legs into a starfish position. Beckett closed his eyes and whispered to himself, "I can do hard things." Slowly, Mrs. Riverton removed her hands from Beckett's back, and he floated all on his own. The crowd went wild!

Mrs. Riverton picked Beckett up out of the
water and held him above her head.
"I CAN do hard things!" Beckett exclaimed.

Mrs. Riverton's students practiced their floating skills every day and, little by little, they became expert floaters.

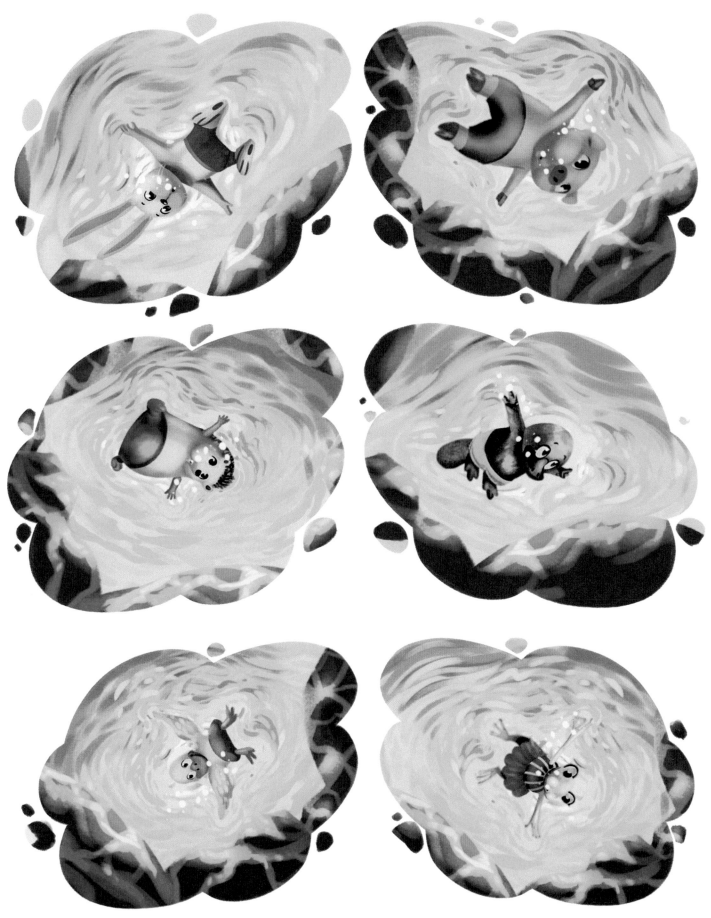

Next, they learned to roll over and swim
with their faces in the water.

Soon, they had all become
amazing aquatic problem solvers!
Everyone was so proud, especially Beckett.

The time had come for Mrs. Riverton to move farther downstream and teach the next group of littles how to be safe in the water. Parents, grandparents, other caring adults, and all of Mrs. Riverton's students gathered to say goodbye.

"Thank you for everything, Mrs. Riverton!" said Lily's mom. "See you next year!" Quilliam's dads chimed in. "We're going to miss you so much!" said Beckett.

"I'm going to miss you all too. I can't wait to hear about all of the hard things you can do when I see you next year!" said Mrs. Riverton, as she dove under the water with a wave.

Drowning Prevention

Drowning is the leading cause of accidental death for children under five years of age and those ever popular puddle jumpers and arm floaties that we all used until we knew better, contribute greatly to that statistic. Even though we think we're doing the right thing by using floatation devices in the pool, what we're actually doing is giving our children a false sense of security and teaching them that it's okay to be in the water without an adult. Our children play at the surface, bicycle kick their way around the water, and even jump in from the side and bob right back up, without understanding that the device they're wearing is what's keeping them afloat. To make matters worse, we encourage them by saying things like, "you're such a great swimmer" when, in actuality, the device is doing the "swimming" for them.

Putting our children in a floatation device in the pool, actively trains their muscle memory to be in a vertical (drowning position) in the water. If they reach the water without the device their bodies have been trained to depend on, they automatically go into this drowning position, and the outcome is often fatal. The good news is, drowning is 100% preventable. The American Academy of Pediatrics (AAP) recommends using the following "layers of protection" to provide a system of increased security in an aquatic environment:

Layers of Protection

Adult supervision - designate a "water watcher" to constantly supervise children in the water. Water watchers should always:

- put down their cell phones
- avoid other activities
- supervise even if lifeguards are present
- switch off with another adult for breaks

Fencing - all swimming pools, including above ground and temporary inflatable pools, should be surrounded by a fence on all four sides. The fence should be at least 60" tall, and have a self-closing, self-latching gate. Gates should open away from the pool, and should never be propped open.

Survival swim lessons - choose high-quality swim lessons that focus on teaching aquatic survival skills first.

Alarms - doors, windows, and gates should be alarmed to alert adults when a barrier has been breached. Doors should be self-closing and self-latching.

CPR - Parents and caregivers should be ready to respond to an aquatic emergency with CPR and safe rescue techniques.

Using multiple layers of protection simultaneously helps prevent injury and death from drowning.

About Survival Swim Lessons

Survival swim lessons provide children with the skills necessary to save themselves should they reach the water alone. Unlike traditional swim lessons, survival swim lessons teach the most critical skill a child needs to have in the event of an aquatic emergency - the ability to turn from a face down position to a float, and remain in that float until help arrives. These specialized lessons are taught by highly trained instructors who undergo strict recertification annually. Lessons begin as early as six months old and are private, one-on-one instruction customized to each student's needs and level of progress. Because 86% of childhood drownings occur when the child is fully clothed, survival swim students practice their self-rescuing skills in clothing before graduating.

About the Author

Michelle McKinney is an Aquatic Behavioral Specialist and Certified ISR (Infant Swimming Resource) Instructor. She is the owner of ISR Austin and teaches students ages six months and up year-round in the Austin area. She is also the founder of The Hope Floats Initiative, which provides free survival swim lessons to underserved communities. When she's not in the water, she's a busy mom of four daughters (two bio and two bonus).

To learn more about Michelle and her program, visit israustin.com.

About the Illustrator

Mousam Banerjee is a full-time artist and illustrator who loves to remain engaged in painting everything from whimsical children's books to realistic concept art. Born into an artistic family, he was keen on creating original paintings right from childhood. With a post graduate diploma in Fine Arts, he has now made a career in digital illustrations.

You can reach out to him at www.illus-station.com or on Instagram at illusstation.kids.

Made in the USA
Middletown, DE
07 June 2023

32203484R00024